Ghost Writer

as told to

Tim Mackintosh-Smith

Illustrations by David Eccles
Design by Octavius Murray

First published in 2005 by
Slightly Foxed Limited
67 Dickinson Court, 15 Brewhouse Yard
London EC1V 4JX
www.foxedquarterly.com

ISBN 0-9548268-8-4

Printed and bound by Smith Settle, Otley

Ghost Writer

> Books are not absolutely dead things, but do contain
> a potency of life in them.

So said Mr Milton, not long after I came to England from Aleppo. I should explain: I am one of those 'not absolutely dead things'. In short, I'm a book, and one with a curious history.

My author, Abd al-Latif ibn Yusuf ibn Muhammad ibn Ali, was born in Baghdad in 1162, in Darb al-Faludhaj, or Pudding Lane. I myself came into the world in 1204, in Cairo, and was named *The Book of Useful Information and Admonition: Things Seen and Events Witnessed in the Land of Egypt*. It is, I know, rather a mouthful, so do feel free to use my accession number, Poc.230. We don't stand on ceremony here in Arabic MSS, not even unique and priceless codices like me.

A talking book? You think it odd, perhaps? A little whimsical – like Apuleius's eloquent ass? There are of course many such literary conceits.[1] I'm not a conceit. I'm the silent talker, the speaker who can speak of the dead and yet interpret the living . . .[2] I can see you are sceptical. Whence my command of English idiom? Whence the epigraph from the *Areopagitica*, the learned footnotes?[3] Well, if you'd spent 312 years in the Bodleian Library you'd probably pick up a thing or two. But perhaps I should begin at the beginning of my story.

'I saw a thin man, all head and heart, writing, his face and his lips playing with divers motions caused by the intensity of his zeal to get out the words, as if he were writing with his every member . . .' That's Abd al-Latif's description of another author, but it

---

[1] The lap dog in Gildon's *New Metamorphosis* and the speaking sofa of Crébillon *fils* also come to mind.

[2] Al-Jahiz, *Kitab al-hayawan*. Jahiz may have intended this as a metaphor.

[3] Sad to say, I have just been warned, under threat of the red pen, that all such interruptions to the narrative flow must cease henceforward.

does well for him too, writing me, infusing a dead black suspension of oak gall, lamp-soot and pomegranate rind with the potency of life. I'm not the final copy; that was made for the Caliph, al-Nasir, in Abd al-Latif's native Baghdad. I've got some marginal afterthoughts, and the odd blob where the nib of the reed snagged on a backward loop; even a wrong verb-ending, forced messily into agreement. But the ink flowed freely through the long fasting afternoons – it was Ramadan, the best month for writers: no cigarette-breaks or coffee-stops – on and on for 140 pages, thirteen lines a page. Not perhaps a pretty hand; but a handsome one, and so instantly legible that you'd never think I was written 800 years ago, and certainly not by a medic.

I've just done something you should never do to scholars of his time, and above all not to Abd al-Latif. I've pigeonholed him. Look at his bibliography – more than 150 works, many of them indeed on medicine but even more on other subjects, from rhetoric to rhubarb and from Aristotle to infinity. Some of them, it must be said, look as if they might have been a little lacking in the

potency of life: *A Compendium of Syntactical Queries, Further Syntactical Queries, An Essay on Boredom*. But one shouldn't speak ill of dead manuscripts, which is what most of them are. Missing, at any rate, presumed dead. And we, the survivors, are anything but lifeless. For instance, there's a short but hair-raising piece on Mongol ethnic cleansing (a phrase Abd al-Latif uses, by the way). And there's me – 'a book', says his biographer, 'that stupefies the intellect'.

Ibn Abi Usaybi'ah wasn't talking about my first section, the *Useful Information* of my title. In this I edify rather than stupefy. Did you know, for example, that the copulating male crocodile invariably ejaculates sixty times? Or that Egyptian grocers priced their goods with labels written on recycled mummy-wrappings? Or that, contrary to the long-accepted assertion of Galen, the human mandibula has no medial suture? (To make absolutely sure of that Abd al-Latif, who could be a bit obsessive, examined over 2,000 jawbones at the necropolis of al-Maqs.) And in case you think this information isn't strictly useful, you can always turn to my short but practical chapter of recipes – try the sultanic hunt pie, for instance, made with three lambs, twenty chickens and seventy other birds.

Rather, it is my second part that stupefies: the section of *Admonition*, a mere fifteen leaves beginning with 'The Events of the Year 597' (AD 1200–1201). It was 'a year that came upon us as a predator snatching away all means of life'. And that is as metaphorical as Abd al-Latif will be. The rest has no need of metaphors.

The Nile failed to rise. There was no harvest. The price of food rose. People left the country and moved to the cities. The price of food ceased to have any meaning: there was no food. People began to eat carrion. When there was no more carrion, people began to eat people. First they ate the dead, then they killed the living. The authorities tried to stop this: convicted man-eaters were burned alive (you can guess what happened to their ready-roasted remains). Some convicted cannibals came up with excuses, like the old woman who was caught gnawing a child. 'She said, "It's my daughter's son. It's better for me to eat him than someone else."' In time no one bothered with excuses. 'Because of the frequency of their repetition upon the senses, such things came to be perceived as perfectly normal.'

He was ruthless, Abd al-Latif, as obsessive in his observation of human evil as of human jawbones. 'I've said enough,' he kept writing; and then he'd be off again, piling scene on nauseating scene. He didn't sermonize. He knew the power of images, knew that they were admonition enough: 'I have decided to concentrate on events I have witnessed personally, since these are the truest form of communication and have the most potent effect.' Quite. But while you will read me and in time recall perhaps one image only – the cauldron, maybe, in which, 'cooked with the finest spices', simmer the heads of five babies – I'm condemned to be the record of them all, in Abd al-Latif's clinical prose, until the end of time or of the Bodleian Library.

At least I can offer you some relief in my final chapter, on the events of the following year, AH 598. There was a general infestation of worms, a plague in the Delta, an earthquake and a pestilential wind; but the Nile did manage to produce a little mucilaginous scum that optimists called water.

Since those dreadful years my destiny has been most peculiar. In fact, you could say I'm lucky to be here at all. My own fair sibling, for instance, the copy made for Caliph al-Nasir, ended up in the Tigris in 1258 when Hulagu the Mongol put Baghdad to the sword. I myself had two brushes with the Mongols, the first only a couple of years later. Abd al-Latif had died in 1231, on his way to Mecca for the Pilgrimage. We, his library, were sold in Aleppo, where for some years he'd been teaching medicine. My new owner read me once, at first with interest then, in my second section, with growing horror ('I seek refuge with God!' he kept muttering, and 'O my mother!'). Finally he banished me to a box-room, along with some unspeakably boring grammars. And there it was that I escaped the attention of Hulagu's horde when, in 1260, he put Aleppo to the sword.

Of the next century or so my recollections are mostly vague (although I do remember vividly an entertaining year on a top shelf, sandwiched between some erotica of the poet Abu Nuwas and

al-Jahiz's *Epistle on Singing Girls*). The names of my
various owners escape me, with the exception of
Umar ibn Ali. Like the others he read me, sought
refuge with God and his mother, and banished me.
But he left his name and a date of purchase, AH 788
(AD 1386), on my title page; and it was from his box-
room that, a few years later, I became aware of
another awful rumpus – Aleppo being put to the
sword again, this time by that neo-Mongol,
Tamerlane. He had the heads of the dead arranged
in neat pyramids, with all the faces looking out-
wards, all 20,000 of them.

You will smile when I tell you this, but when Abd
al-Latif first wrote me I imagined I might do some
good in the world. I agree, much of my useful information is next to useless. But I do offer some
instructive, if shocking, insights into the nature of
human wickedness. With the innocence of youth I
believed, as did my author, in the admonitory power
of historical exempla. 'Everyone should read histories,' he wrote elsewhere, 'so that they may learn of
the good that men have done, and the evil.' Hulagu,
Tamerlane and time have made me a cynic. I know

now that the only people who learn anything from histories are historians. And what do they do with what they learn? Put it in more histories. We feed each other, you see. We too are cannibals.

But we still want to be heard. We hold the magic that the bard alone once had, before the days of writing: we hold memory. Abu Hamid of Granada said, 'Books in themselves do not contain knowledge. They only contain writing which points one towards knowledge.' But isn't knowledge only applied memory? Think of Abd al-Latif, my author, of what he memorized – 'I had the Qur'an by heart,' he wrote, 'and the *Fasih*, and the *Maqamat*, and the *Diwan* of al-Mutanabbi, and abridged manuals of syntax and jurisprudence,' and all that when he was still only a boy; think of the decades of data that were to come – and all of it subsisting in a few millivolts passing through a gland. And when the switch flicks off, and long after the gland has rotted, we still remember and speak our memories. We are the voices of the dead, audible and articulate. We don't expect to be listened to; but we still want to be heard.

Forgive me for harping on. It's just my own memory of those endless boxes, those excruciating grammars. I had to put up with two more centuries of them. They came, however, to an unexpected end.

'*Useful Information . . . the Land of Egypt.* The Firanji will pay good money for this one.' A Firanji? A Frank? For me, a child of the age of the Crusades, offspring of a man who hobnobbed with Saladin, this was alarming. So too was the man who held me – a man with a tall fawn cap and outrageous moustaches; a dervish, I learned. None of those in my young day. But he knew his books. I could tell from the way he cradled me and turned my pages. 'Cairo, the year 600,' he said, reading my colophon. 'Over four hundred years old. And an autograph. Yes, the Firanji will like this.'

He did. And I liked him, despite another tall hat – black this time, with a sort of ledge running round it – and hair as long as Hulagu's, and a name I first heard as *buquk*, Your Trumpet.

Mr Pococke, to begin with, seemed most exotic indeed. He was not only a Nazarene but a clergyman to boot, chaplain to the English Turkey Merchants

in Aleppo. You mustn't think I had any objections
on doctrinal grounds. After all, my own author
never saw religious differences as a barrier to intel-
lectual intercourse; he always spoke, for example, of
his discussions on anatomy with Moses Maimonides
as highly informative. In fact it was when I saw on
Mr Pococke's shelf a copy of that learned Jew's dis-
courses that I realized the Englishman too belonged
to the commonwealth of learning in which there are
no borders: 'Knowledge', said Abd al-Latif, 'moves
from nation to nation, from land to land.' And so
did I, in the spring of 1636, when Mr Pococke sailed
with his manuscript collection for England and
Archbishop Laud's brand-new chair of Arabic in the
University of Oxford.

I voyaged in varied and mostly stimulating com-
pany. Among the scores of works in Arabic, Hebrew
and Syriac, Maydani's *Proverbs* was a garrulous and
entertaining shipmate. I even broke the ice with a
rather po-faced Samaritan Pentateuch. And as I
began to acquire some facility with the non-Semitic
tongues, especially Latin and English, I got to know
the clones. You may think the word an anachronism;

but that was how they struck me, those first printed books of my acquaintance. I too could be reproduced of course but, copyists being what they are, my twins would never be so unnervingly identical. *Al-kamal li'llah*: perfection is God's prerogative. Any misgivings about the printed word, however, swiftly evaporated when it dawned on me that here, at last, was a chance of being heard more widely than I could have dreamed. I arrived in Oxford hardly able to contain myself.

'I think', Mr Pococke wrote to a friend, 'that he that hath once been out of England, if he get home, will not easily be persuaded to leave it again.' Unless, that is, the person concerned has a passion for manuscript-hunting and an entrée to the greatest city of the East: the following year he was off again, this time to Constantinople to minister to the spiritual needs of Sir Sackville Crow, His Majesty's envoy to the Sublime Porte – and, more importantly, to add to his own oriental library. You may imagine my disappointment, made the greater by my knowledge that Mr Pococke had just supervised the cutting of the first Arabic typeface at the University Press. As things turned out, the three years it took for him to return were only the beginning of a wait that was to last a century and a half.

I waited through the troubled years that preceded the Civil War; sat out the conflict itself in the pleasant rectory of Childrey in Berkshire, where Mr Pococke planted a cedar of Lebanon (you may see it there today) and worked on his great *Specimen* of Arabian history; waited in Oxford once more, after the Restoration, while he laboured on his *Lexicon Heptaglotton*, then on his commentaries on Malachi and Micah. Admittedly, his rooms at Christ Church were an improvement on those horrid Aleppan boxes, but I was, in every sense of the phrase, on the shelf.

It was only towards the end of his life that Dr Pococke, as he now was, turned his attention to me. As he himself was busy with the more pressing concerns of Hosea and Joel, he passed me on to his son, Mr Edward Pococke junior – who, to my astonishment, began at once to transcribe me. If I tell you that for us manuscripts the pleasures associated with the physical act of reproduction are not unakin to those felt by you humans in your own version of this activity, and if I remind you that close on 500 years had passed since my last enjoyment of them, you will have some idea of the thrill I experienced. Nor was my excitement limited to this, for young Mr Pococke wasted no time in putting me into Latin – *Abdollatiphi Historiæ Ægypti compendium* – and then, before you could say *eheu fugaces*, submitted both versions to the Press. O the joy of seeing those first sheets of my printed self, Arabic and Roman recto to recto!

This literary coition was rudely interrupted. Where the father enjoyed, in Mr Locke's estimation, a life that appeared 'one constant calm', the son was more volatile. He had expected to inherit the Laudian chair, but on the old man's death in 1691 found himself, as they said at the time, wanting friends. The professorship went instead to Bodley's Librarian, Dr Hyde, young Mr Pococke went off in a huff to his rectory of Mildenhall in Wiltshire – and my bilingual edition ended in mid-sentence on page 96. He simply pulled it from the press. You may see one of the very few remaining copies of this half-cock *compendium*

in Oxford, in Duke Humfrey's Library, bound with a *Sermon on Evil-speaking*, a *Treatise on Good Women* and a Latin word-list; shades of those wormy grammars in Aleppo. I myself was sold to the Bodleian with the rest of Dr Pococke's oriental manuscripts.

One Oxford orientalist had kept me on the shelf, another had given me the push, and the next one literally died on me. Dr Hyde might not have wanted friends, but I do feel he wanted a certain focus: librarian, arabist, hebraist, turkicist, persianist, translator of the Gospels into Malay, 'an oracle in Armenian' – he was a one-man Babel. His curiosity concerning biblical minutiae more than matched Dr Pococke's. 'I shall send you some of my observations,' he wrote to Mr Robert Boyle,

> viz, an account of the bird dukiphath in *Leviticus* and *Deuteronomy*; an account of the hyssop . . . ; and, thirdly, you shall have a true and full account of the dove's-dung eaten in the siege of Samaria.

It was only late in life that, with an eye on the solidity of his posterior reputation, he began to apply himself to his work on the Zoroastrians, *Historia Religionis Veterum Persarum*. This, his *magnum opus*, came out in 1700 and was promptly panned by the critics. The good doctor boiled his tea-kettle with the greatest part of the impression.

He never recovered from the blow. I was the companion of his few remaining years. He began a new Latin version of me, a commentary on the same, even ordered plates – and was found dead at his desk in Christ Church in the cold February of 1703, slumped across my pages. 'Hyde, the wonder of the world, is dead,' declared a colleague in the Low Countries; more privately but nearer to home, another fellow-orientalist, Mr Prideaux, memorialized my late – my latest – editor as an 'egregious donce'. Had you access to my second incomplete translation, you might judge for yourself which is the fitter epitaph. But of Dr Hyde's own *Abdollatiphi Historiæ*, not a trace is to be found. Alone among his papers, it disappeared, by whose agency no one knew.

Poor Dr Hyde. 'He was wonderfull slow of speech,' Mr Hearne the antiquary recalled, 'and his

delivery so very low, that 'twas impossible to hear
what he said, in so much that when he preached on
Sunday morning at Christ Church, on my first com-
ing to Oxford, after he had been in the pulpit an
hour and a half, most of the congregation went out.'
And thus to edify and admonish, yet not be heard,
was also my fate.

People began to whisper that I was cursed. As the
product of an enlightened age and a sceptical author
I naturally regarded this as nonsense, and when in
1746 Mr Thomas Hunt, the then incumbent of the
Arabic chair, began yet another version of me and
went so far as to solicit subscriptions for its printing,
I fully believed that my third Laudian Professor
would be my lucky one. Oxford, you see, had
changed. The commonwealth of learning, now
emancipated from the tyranny of dukiphaths, was
ruled by Reason. The final remnant of scholastical
gloom had fled before the penetrating rays of empir-
ical inquiry. Britannia looked East, toward the
dawning of an empire, and thirsted for knowledge of
those distant lands. The bright flame of my Useful
Information, hidden so long beneath the bushel of

vicissitude, would at last illumine the umbrageous groves of Academe.

To Mr Hunt's proposed edition there were precisely two subscribers.

I succumbed to despair; began to believe that I was indeed cursed, if not by some exterior maleficence then by my repellent subject-matter. For forty years I sat unopened, untouched, undusted. It was thus with a creaking spine and feelings of the profoundest pessimism that I underwent transcription by yet another Laudian Professor, Mr Joseph White. And it was in a similarly profound state of disbelief that I beheld my first full printed Arabic edition, done in 1789 by Mr White in Tübingen – may God bless the one and water the other with rain! I had hardly recovered from the surprise when, in Halle the following year, and in a display of that alacrity for which his nation is famous, Herr Professor Doktor Wahl brought out his *Abdallatifs, eines arabischen Arztes, Denkwürdigkeiten Egyptens &c. &c. &c.* Mr White subsequently latinized me in 1800 and englished my chapter on antiquities in 1801. M. le Baron Silvestre de Sacy was somewhat *en arrière* with his Paris edition of 1810, but made up for it by appending *plusieurs morceaux inédits de divers écrivains orientaux.* I was no longer a mere book; I was a bandwagon.

And with that, you may imagine, I could settle down to a comfortable retirement in the Bodleian, slumbering in that hushed atmosphere of leather and anecdotes like a bishop in the Athenaeum, while my new and vigorous offspring went the rounds of Europe. And so I did, roused only by occasional reports of my celebrity. (Or, more often, notoriety. 'Nothing in history equals what Abdallatif describes,' wrote Sir Henry Yule in a note on cannibalism. 'The horrid details fill a chapter of some length, and *we need not quote from them.*' The italics are mine; the response is typical.) But the strangest episode of my history was yet to come.

I had an inkling that something was afoot when in 1928 I heard from that omniscient informant, the Catalogue, that Messrs Hutchinson had published a certain Mr R. S. Saunders's *Healing through the spirit agency: by the great Persian* [sic] *physician Abduhl Latif* , *'the man of Baghdad', and information*

*concerning the life of the hereafter of the deepest inter-
est to all inquirers and students of psychic phenomena.*
The Bodleian being a copyright library we naturally
get a lot of nutcases in – stack-fodder, we call them
– and needless to say I did not wish to make the
acquaintance of what was undoubtedly an uneducated
farrago of mystic-eastern Blavatskian theosophical
twaddle. So, although my suspicions were awakened,
I had no proper intimation of the events that would
begin to unfold some thirty years later, in 1960.

'I agree, it is most strange,' said the Keeper of
Oriental Books as he opened me at my title-page
towards the end of that year. Beside him, a man
whom I did not know was looking at me with a
most curious expression – one that I could only
compare to the features of a Sufi devotee in a state of
rapture. 'Such a remarkable work,' the Keeper went
on, 'and never an English translation. Except of
course for the fragment in White's *Ægyptiaca*. So
although I must stress once more, Mr Videan, that
the circumstances of your request are . . .' as he
sought the word I heard an illibrarious snort from
the Assistant Keeper ' . . . *exceptional*, the prospect of

Abd al-Latif becoming available to a wider audience has persuaded me to allow the copy to be made. That, and –' he darted a glance at the now dangerously ecstatic Mr Videan '– your very evident enthusiasm for the project.'

A distant memory of the joys of reproduction passed through my venerable stitching. Whether Mr Videan was the man to revive them, however, I was not so sure. 'The Doctor will be eternally grateful to you,' he exclaimed, bouncing on the balls of his feet. 'Eternally! I shall bring my paraphernalia immediately.' And with that he bounded out of the Department door.

My forebodings concerning Mr Videan were amply justified. In no time at all he returned, laid me flat on my back and flashed at me – again and again, with what he called his 'trusty Leica'. So this was reproduction, 1960s-style. *O tempora! O mores!* O would that I had never been written!

My tactful fellow-inmates in Arabic MSS remained silent about the indignity I had suffered; but its eventual consequences could not remain hidden. It was one morning in the autumn of 1965

that the news broke, sending a shiver through the
Library from the infernal penetralia of the stacks up
to the whispering-gallery of the Radcliffe Camera –
a shiver that became a buzz, not so much of sound
as of disquiet, a subliminal but general agitation. In
the Lower Reading Room there was much peering
over spectacles as librarians tried to identify the cul-
prits; in Duke Humfrey's Library it was remarked
that the death-watch beetles were unseasonably
lively. Neither beetles nor readers were to blame,
but books. An author, it seemed, had done the
unthinkable – had interfered from beyond the
grave. My author.

It was some time before I could bring myself to
look upon the cause of the scandal – my first com-
plete English translation, entitled *The Eastern Key*,
by Judge Kamal Hafuth Zand and John A. and Ivy
E. Videan. Lest you suspect me of fabrication, I
quote from Mrs Videan's introduction to the vol-
ume, published under the respectable imprint of
Messrs George Allen & Unwin:

The story of how this present translation came

to be made is an interesting one . . . Our first
meeting with Abd al-Latif was in August, 1957,
when he spoke to my husband and to me dur-
ing a conversation with a sensitive, Mrs Ray
Welch, in London. Since then we have had
many long talks with him, through Mrs Welch
and also through Mr Jim Hutchings. It was
not unexpected, therefore, that he should tell
us in 1960 that he wished my husband to make
a photographic copy of the Bodleian manuscript. Abd al-Latif added later that he would
send a translator from Baghdad. He came in
the welcome form of Judge Kamal Hafuth
Zand, who was introduced to us by Mrs Ray
Welch from Abd al-Latif . . . Abd al-Latif himself is The Key to bring this book to life in the
Anglo-Saxon tongue.

Anyone would think I was *Beowulf.* But seriously
. . . I mean, I know all about ghost-writers in the
usual sense of the word; of necessity, I have had to
engage one myself. But this? Where would it end?
Mediums would take over the media, and the Ouija

board would be as ubiquitous in editorial departments as the email. We'd have Mr Lees-Milne entertaining us with his posthumous diaries on the saints and sinners of the afterlife, and Mr M. R. James tingling our spines, both bookish and human, with his first-hand tales of the spirit-world. Mr Dickens might even get down to finishing *Edwin Drood*. People would write furious letters to the *Telegraph* about their own obituaries. And think of the ructions it would cause in publishing law, with copyright extending to the last trump and Mr R. S. Saunders filing libel suits against my amanuensis, Mr Mackintosh-Smith.[4]

In the end, you will have to decide for yourself whom to believe – me, or Ivy. Personally I'm willing to grant that she may have been, so to speak, genuinely deluded. I can picture the scene: a small close parlour in a suburb; the hats, the gloves, a cologne-scented handkerchief; white fingers on the

---

[4] I hasten to point out that the bit about 'uneducated . . . twaddle' was his interpolation. [I thought I warned you . . . TM-S]

planchette. All quite suggestive. And Mrs Welch, asking if anybody was there . . .

So, *is* anybody there? Only us. We alone are the voices of the dead: of our authors; of the babies in the cauldron, the severed heads of Aleppo, of all the dead from the dawn of writing to yesterday's paper, crying in the wilderness of the library while famine and Tamerlane do their worst and always will.

Don't think it odd that we speak; only that people don't hear.

My scepticism regarding authorial intervention from 'the other side' is shared by my ghost-writer, MR MACKINTOSH-SMITH, who tells me he has spent the past decade investigating the career of the fourteenth-century adventurer Ibn Battutah without so much as a tap of encouragement from his subject.